BRAM STOKER

DRACULA

STERLING AND THE DISTINCTIVE
STERLING LOGO ARE REGISTERED TRADEMARKS
OF STERLING PUBLISHING CO., INC.

LIBRARY OF CONGRESS
CATALOGING-IN-PUBLICATION DATA AVAILABLE

2 4 6 8 10 9 7 5 3 1

PUBLISHED BY STERLING PUBLISHING CO., INC.
387 PARK AVENUE SOUTH, NEW YORK, NY 10016
© 2008 BY BEN CALDWELL
DISTRIBUTED IN CANADA BY STERLING PUBLISHING
C/O CANADIAN MANDA GROUP, 165 DUFFERIN STREET
TORONTO, ONTARIO, CANADA M6K 3H6
DISTRIBUTED IN THE UNITED KINGDOM
BY GMC DISTRIBUTION SERVICES
CASTLE PLACE, 166 HIGH STREET, LEWES,
EAST SUSSEX, ENGLAND BN7 1XU
DISTRIBUTED IN AUSTRALIA BY
CAPRICORN LINK (AUSTRALIA) PTY. LTD.
P.O. BOX 704, WINDSOR, NSW 2756, AUSTRALIA

PRINTED IN CHINA   *   ALL RIGHTS RESERVED

STERLING ISBN 978-1-4027-6430-1

BRAM STOKER

DRACULA

ADDRESS ADAPTED BY

MICHAEL MUCCI
WRITER

BEN CALDWELL
PENCILLER/COLORIST

BILL HALLIAR
INKER

STERLING

New York / London
www.sterlingpublishing.com/kids

FOR MY FOLKS,
WHO ALWAYS EMBRACED
THE IDEA OF MONSTERS
IN THE CLOSETS AND
TENTACLES UNDER
THE BEDS. I WILL BE
FOREVER GRATEFUL.
- M. M.

FOR DAVID MOORE, WHO
TAUGHT ME TO LOVE
HISTORY.
- B. C.

JULY, 1897. LONDON -- WE STAND AT THE EDGE OF A NEW CENTURY, AS THE LIGHT OF MODERN CIVILIZATION DISPELS THE GLOOM OF PAST SUPERSTITIONS...

... BUT I CANNOT FORGET THE EVENTS OF SEVEN YEARS AGO.

LITTLE REMAINS OF OUR HARROWING ADVENTURES, SAVE A RUINOUS OLD CASTLE, A MASS OF ESTATE RECEIPTS, AND MY OLD JOURNAL...

5 MAY. BISTRITZ, ROMANIA -- TODAY I WILL TAKE THE COACH FROM BISTRITZ TO THE BORGO PASS, WHERE I WILL TRANSFER TO A PRIVATE CARRAIGE.

SCHEDULES IN THIS REMOTE PART OF EUROPE ARE HAZARDOUS...

... BUT IF ALL GOES WELL, I SHALL SUP IN THE CASTLE OF COUNT DRACULA TONIGHT!

COUNT DRACULA!

DINING WITH JONATHAN HARKER, LOWLY ESTATE AGENT'S CLERK!

PERHAPS MY FELLOW PASSENGERS CAN TELL ME SOMETHING OF MY COUNT DRACULA...

EXCUSE ME... DO YOU SPEAK ENGLISH?

GERMAN, PERHAPS?

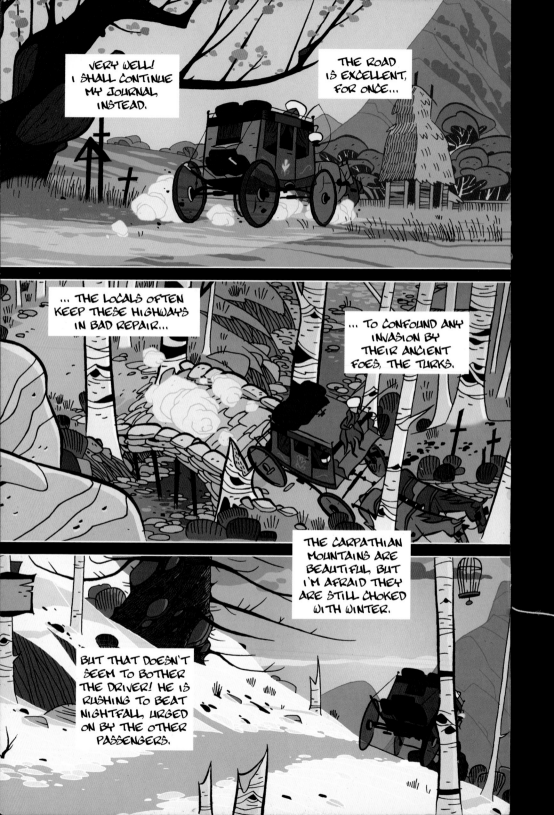

YET FOR ME, THE DRONING OF THE COACH WHEELS IS LIKE A SOOTHING LULLABY...

WH --

THE BORGO PASS! WE'RE -- WE'RE DRIVING RIGHT ON PAST THE RENDEZVOUS!

DRIVER, STOP!

DRIVER!!!

NO, ENGLISHMAN!

TONIGHT, IT IS A BAD NIGHT!

TOMORROW IS BETTER!

YES, TOMORROW!

!

YOU DO SPEAK ENGLISH!

STOP THIS COACH! YOU ARE CARRYING A PASSENGER WHO BELONGS TO ME!

TOO LATE!

QUICKLY! WHILE THEY MOVE YOUR LUGGAGE TO HIS COACH!

DO YOU KNOW WHAT **TODAY** IS?

MAY FOURTH?

YES, YES! BUT IT IS THE DAY OF ST. GEORGE!

TONIGHT, ALL MANNER OF DANGER, IT IS SURROUNDING YOU!

IT... IT IS?

QUICKLY! TAKE THIS!

TAKE IT!

BUT --

FOR THE SAKE OF THOSE WHO LOVE YOU... WHO WAIT FOR YOUR SAFE RETURN...

MINA?

TAKE IT!

AND TAKE CARE, ENGLISHMAN...

FOR THE DEAD TRAVEL FAST!

REALLY!

THESE TRAN-
SYLVANIANS ARE SUCH
A SUPERSTITIOUS LOT!

AFTER ALL, WHAT
POSSIBLE NEED MIGHT
I HAVE...

... FOR
THIS?

KLMP
KLMP

KLMP
KLMP

KLMP
KLMP

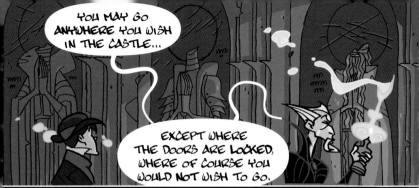

YOU MAY GO ANYWHERE YOU WISH IN THE CASTLE...

EXCEPT WHERE THE DOORS ARE LOCKED, WHERE OF COURSE YOU WOULD NOT WISH TO GO.

A REMARKABLE HOUSE, COUNT! THE FURNI --

-- YAI!!!

ER... TH... THE FURNISHINGS ARE QUITE...

... INTERESTING.

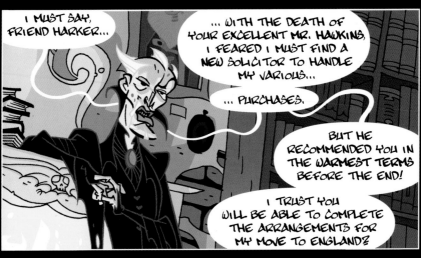

AH!

LISTEN! LISTEN!

oooooooooooo!

oooooooooooo!

TO... TO THE WOLVES?

YES...

THE CHILDREN OF THE NIGHT!

WHAT BEAUTIFUL MUSIC THEY MAKE!

AH...

YOU DWELLERS IN THE CITY CAN-NOT ENTER INTO THE FEELINGS OF THE HUNTER.

BUT ENOUGH!

IT IS TIME FOR US TO TALK OF OUR BUSINESS!

HAVE YOU PREPARED THE CONTRACTS?

DEAREST MINA! TWO WEEKS HAVE PASSED IN MAKING ARRANGEMENTS FOR THE COUNT, AND IN PRACTICING ENGLISH WITH HIM FOR MOST OF EACH NIGHT. IN TRUTH, SOME OF THE NOVELTY HAS FADED FROM MY "ARABIAN NIGHTS" LIFE HERE!

WORKING THROUGH THE NIGHT, AND ONLY WAKING AT THE NEXT DUSK, SEEMS SO... SO...

UN-ENGLISH!

AAAAI!

A-APOLOGIES, COUNT! I DIDN'T HEAR --

COUNT DRACULA?

YOU...

...YOU HAVE CUT YOURSELF..!

COUNT?

HSSS!

TAKE CARE HOW YOU CUT YOURSELF...
IT CAN BE DEADLY IN THIS COUNTRY.

?

BUT YOUR...
... YOUR REFLECTION...

BAH!

I AM GLAD NOW THAT I HAVE WRITTEN THIS JOURNAL IN SUCH DETAIL ... FOR THERE IS SOMETHING STRANGE ABOUT THIS PLACE -- AND ALL WHO ARE IN IT!

BUT NO, I AM NOT THE ARTISTIC TYPE WHO SEES GHOSTS AROUND EVERY CORNER... AND SO I HAD BETTER KEEP MY SENSE.

HOW I WISH I HAD NEVER COME!

I HAD EXPECTED THE COUNT TO BE AN ECCENTRIC, BUT HIS BEHAVIOR HAS MADE ME UNEASY... I COULD ALMOST SWEAR THAT I AM THE ONLY LIVING SOUL IN THIS CASTLE.

BUT I WILL EXPLORE BELOW, TO SEE IF I MIGHT BORROW A MIRROR FROM ONE OF THE SERVANTS...

... AND PERHAPS, TO SEE EXACTLY WHAT SORT OF SITUATION I HAVE FALLEN INTO!

I WILL KEEP MY JOURNAL WITH ME -- IT IS WRITTEN IN SHORT-HAND, WHICH THE COUNT WILL NOT KNOW -- BUT STILL, I DO NOT TRUST THE MAN...

... IF INDEED, HE IS A MAN.

KLIK!

CREEEEEEAAAAAAAAAAK!

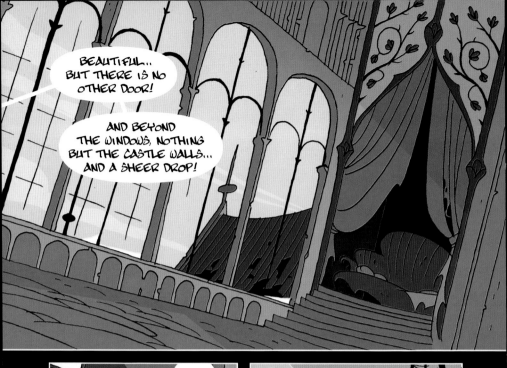

... AND SO I WRITE AGAIN TO YOU, MINA, ALTHOUGH I SUSPECT BY YOUR SILENCE THAT THE COUNT HAS DESTROYED MY EARLIER CORRESPONDENCE...

... AND I HOPE THAT WRITING THIS LETTER IN SHORT-HAND WILL CONFUSE HIM ENOUGH...

... THAT IT MAY PASS SAFELY TO YOU.

YAWN!

KRNK!
THMP!

WHAT IS THAT --

AH.

SZGANY PEASANTS!

PACKING CRATES?

THMP!

NOT CRATES...

... COFFINS!

THE COUNT'S PLANS HAVE RIPENED, WHATEVER THEY ARE. I HAVE BEEN HERE A MONTH AND MORE...

... AND I FEAR HE WILL HAVE NO MORE USE FOR MY LIFE!

AH...

... FRIEND HARKER!

TOMORROW, MY FRIEND, WE MUST PART... YOU TO YOUR ENGLAND, ME TO SOME LAST BUSINESS BEFORE I ALSO GO THERE.

AS THERE IS MUCH TO ATTEND TO...

?

... PERHAPS WE SHALL NOT MEET IN THIS WORLD AGAIN!

BUT DO NOT FRET! I HAVE MADE ALL THE REQUIRED ARRANGE- MENTS.

TONIGHT YOU SHALL HAVE A LAST MEAL...

... AND BE GONE!

MY CLOTHES ARE ALL GONE! MY BAGGAGE, TOO.

"REQUIRED ARRANGEMENTS" INDEED!

NO MATTER! I HAD GUESSED AS MUCH... NO DOUBT I AM TO BE LEFT TO THE FATAL EMBRACE OF THE THREE LADIES.

BUT I REFUSE SUCH A FATE!

SO I TAKE WITH ME THIS JOURNAL, MY LOVE... AND HOPE THAT SHOULD I FAIL THIS DESPERATE ESCAPE, IT FINDS ITS WAY TO YOU.

WITH THE DOORS LOCKED, THIS REALLY IS THE ONLY WAY DOWN...

... I MAY BE ONLY A MAN, BUT IF THAT WRETCHED COUNT DRACULA CAN DO IT...

... SO SHALL I!

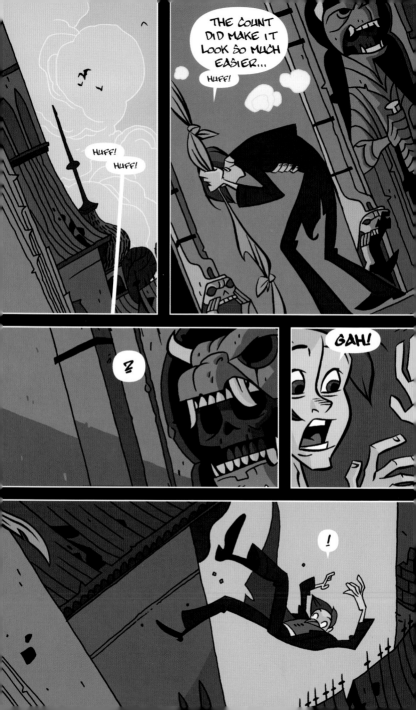

HSSS....

BUT HOW SELFISH I AM, WHEN YOU'VE HAD THREE PROPOSALS OF MARRIAGE IN ONE WEEK...

THREE!

OH, MINA! ISN'T IT TOO WONDERFUL? FIRST DR. SEWARD -- AND IT'S A SHAME ABOUT YOUR FIANCÉ, I THINK YOU AND THE DOCTOR WOULD GET ON SPLENDID...

LUCY!

... OH, ALL RIGHT! AND THEN THAT SWEET TEXAN, MR. QUINCY...

... BUT WHEN ARTHUR HOLMWOOD PROPOSED...

LUCY!

HA! HA!

OH, COME ON MINA! DO HURRY!!

IT'S ONLY A HAT!

LUCY! DO BE SENSIBLE! WE'VE NO UMBRELLAS, AND LOOK AT THE SKY! LET'S GO BACK HOME!

LUCY!

HA HA!

DOUBLE QUICK!

BLASTED RAIN!

STEP LIVELY, LADS! THERE LOOKS TA' BE SURVIVORS! GRAB THEM LINES!

HEY!

WATCH THAT RIGGING! TIGHTER!

NOTHING BUT BOXES!

WAIT! OVER HERE!

DID... DID ANYONE JUST SEE THAT DOG?

IF ANY SAILORS HAVE SURVIVED, THEY'LL NEED MEDICAL ATTENTION!

YOU TWO, GO HOME...

... AND STAY OUT OF THE STORM!

LET'S GO, LUCY...

LUCY?

"THERE WERE NO PASSENGERS OR CARGO...

... ONLY FIFTY COFFINS FULL OF DIRT."

"AND THE CREW?"

"LOST, EVERY ONE OF THEM"

"ALL EXCEPT THE CAPTAIN. IT SEEMS LIKE HE LASHED HIMSELF TO THE RUDDER WHEEL, TO KEEP THE SHIP ON COURSE...

... EVEN AFTER HE'D DIED."

"NO ONE KNOWS WHAT HAPPENED TO HIM OR THE CREW. THE ONLY SURVIVOR LOOKS TO BE SOME SORT OF PET DOG THAT RAN OFF WHEN THE SHIP HIT SHORE."

POOR CREATURE! I HOPE THE S.P.C.A. CAN FIND IT!

AS FOR THE REST... NO DOUBT SOME MADMAN IS TO BLAME!

THERE IS NO MYSTERY IN THAT!

PERHAPS... ALTHOUGH MADNESS ITSELF HAS PROVED A GREAT MYSTERY.

I HAVE DOWNSTAIRS A PATIENT -- MR. RENFIELD -- WHO PROVES MY POINT.

WOULD YOU LIKE TO MEET HIM?

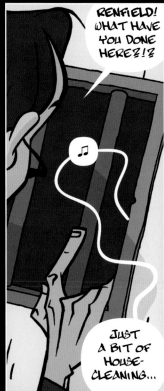

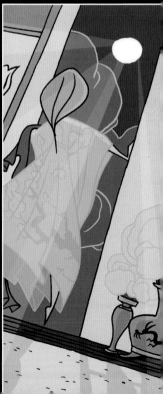

LUCY!

I SHOULD HAVE KNOWN I'D FIND YOU HERE AGAIN!

LUCY! WAKE UP!

REILLY! WHAT THE DEV--

RENFIELD'S GONE AND TORE UP HIS ROOM SOMETHING AWFUL!

LOOK!

QUICK, MAN! GET SOME OF THE OTHER ATTENDANTS OUTSIDE!

NO!

AND BE CAREFUL! HE'S SURE TO HAVE HURT HIMSELF...

... IN THE LONG DROP.

HEE HEE

WAIT UP, YOU!

... AND THAT'S HOW JACK GOT THAT RIDICULOUS BEARD!

HOW FUNNY! DID YOU KNOW THAT, LUCY?

LUCY?

...

SHE'S BEEN OUT OF SORTS FOR DAYS.

I HAD NOTICED...

DEAR LUCY! SHOULD WE FETCH DR. SEWARD?

EXCUSE ME, MISS, LETTER COME FOR YOU.

FOR... ME?

I... I HAD BETTER OPEN IT...

!

IT'S... IT'S FROM BUDA-PESTH! THE HOSPITAL OF ST. JOSEPH AND STE. MARY... JONATHAN IS THERE!

HE... HE WAS FOUND NEAR THE BORDER WITH TRANSYLVANIA. TRANSYLVANIA! OH, AND THEY WRITE THAT HE HAS HAD A TERRIBLE BRAIN-FEVER...

HOW AWFUL!

... BUT HE IS DAILY RECOVERING! OH! HE WISHES ME TO COME IMMEDIATELY, SO WE MAY MARRY!

I MUST GO! AT ONCE!

ONE
MOMENT!

ONE
MOMENT!

TAT!
TAT!

TAT!
TAT!
TAT!

TAT!
TAT!
TAT!

TAT!
TAT!
TAT!

I WAS
AFRAID
THA--

DR. VAN
HELSING!

YOU'VE
COME!

MY DEAR
FRIEND DR.
SEWARD...

... IT HAS
BEEN MANY YEARS
THAT YOU ARE BOTH
MY FRIEND AND BEST
STUDENT, YES?

AND SO
WHEN YOU
SUMMON ME
OUT OF AM-
STERDAM FOR
SOME GREAT
CRISIS...

IS IT SUCH
A WONDER THAT
I SHOULD BE
HERE?

LET US
BEGIN!

HAVE YOU SAID ANYTHING TO HER YOUNG FIANCÉ ABOUT YOUR... CONCERNS?

HM

AH!

NO, NOT YET.

GOOD!

YOU HAVE GIVEN HER A BLOOD TRANSFUSION, SO.

THEN... SHE HAS LOST SO MUCH BLOOD RECENTLY?

INTERESTING...

AH, JACK. YOU WOULD NOT WASTE MY TIME WITH TRIFLES! THIS BLOOD LOSS, IT IS...

STRANGE?

STRANGE IS THE VERY WORD! MISS LUCY IS -- OR WAS -- IN PERFECT HEALTH! NO INJURY OR DEFECT, FRESH AIR...

... AND AS FOR DISEASE, I CAN THINK OF NO INFECTION OR DIS ORDER TO EXPLAIN IT!

SINCE I WROTE YOU FOUR DAYS AGO...

... I'VE HAD TO GIVE HER THREE TRANSFUSIONS! IT'S UNHEARD OF!

WHERE CAN IT ALL HAVE GONE?

...

GOOD EVENING TO YOU, MISS! I HOPE THOSE DOCTORS HAVE DONE YOU A BIT OF GOOD! NOW LETS --

DEAR!

WHAT IS THAT SMELL?

WELL, I'LL BE!

GARLIC! HOW VERY STRANGE!

WHAT SORT OF OUTLADISH QUACKERY THESE FOREIGNERS DREAM UP!

I'LL JUST CLEAR THIS...

... SO THE MISS CAN HAVE A NICE SLEEP!

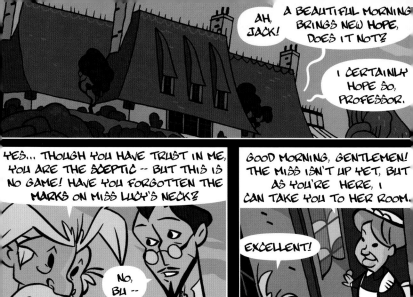

AH, JACK! A BEAUTIFUL MORNING BRINGS NEW HOPE, DOES IT NOT?

I CERTAINLY HOPE SO, PROFESSOR.

YES... THOUGH YOU HAVE TRUST IN ME, YOU ARE THE SCEPTIC -- BUT THIS IS NO GAME! HAVE YOU FORGOTTEN THE MARKS ON MISS LUCY'S NECK?

NO, BU --

GOOD MORNING, GENTLEMEN! THE MISS ISN'T UP YET, BUT AS YOU'RE HERE, I CAN TAKE YOU TO HER ROOM.

EXCELLENT!

I MUST SAY...

... YOU TWO GENTLEMEN MUSTN'T TAKE ALL THE CREDIT FOR MISS LUCY'S CONDITION! HER ROOM WAS SO STUFFY LAST NIGHT... SO I TOOK OUT THOSE DREADFUL FLOWERS AND OPENED UP THE WINDOWS!

I'LL GET THE TEA!

!

MEIN GOTT!

QUICKLY! THE BLOOD SHE HAS LOST, IT IS TOO MUCH FOR HER! WE NEED ANOTHER TRANSFUSION... CALL UP HOLMWOOD AND MORRIS AT ONCE! LET US HOPE THE STRENGTH OF FOUR GOOD MEN...

... IS EQUAL TO THE MALEVOLENCE OF ONE DEVIL!

OOOH...

YOU SHALL SEE WHAT HAS BEEN DONE AGAINST GOD AND MAN.
ZZZ
♫
LUCY?!?
QUIET!

THE VAMPIRE, HE DOES NOT DIE, BUT INSTEAD DEVOURS THE BLOOD OF OTHERS TO OBTAIN EVERLASTING LIFE...
... AND TO KEEP HIM IN UNNATURAL YOUTH!
HE HAS A TERRIBLE STRENGTH, AND TWISTS NATURE TO HIS PURPOSE. IN WOLF FORM HE FLED THE DEMETER...
... BUT OTHER FORMS HE ALSO COMMANDS, THE RAT AND THE BAT...
... AND AS WE SAW WITH POOR LUCY, THE VERY MISTS!
IN DRACULA, PRINCE OF WALLACHIA, THESE POWERS ARE MOST ACUTE, FOR HE IS CENTURIES IN THE MAKING. OH YES... I HAVE CONTACTED DR. ARMINIUS OF BUDA-PESHT UNIVERSITY...
... THERE IS NO DOUBT!
THE DRACULAS ARE AN ANCIENT AND NOBLE FAMILY. SOME WERE RUMORED TO BE OF THE STRIGOI -- ANCIENT WITCHES...
... AND DRACULA HIMSELF, AT THE LAKE OF THE SCHOLOMANCE, CLAIMED HIS POWERS FROM THE DEVIL

BUT THIS POWER, HE PURCHASES IT AT A TERRIBLE PRICE!

FOR DRACULA IS NOT FREE...

... CURSED BY GOD FOR HIS CRIMES, ALL THE SYMBOLS OF GOD ARE HATEFUL TO HIM -- THE CRUCIFIX AND HOLY WATER AND SUCH.

RUNNING WATERS CONFOUND HIM...

... BUT ABOVE ALL, HE DREADS THE LIGHT OF DAY, WHICH DOES ROB HIM OF HIS MANY STRENGTHS AND POWERS...

... AND SO HE MUST RETURN EACH DAWN TO THE HALLOWED SOIL OF HIS ANCESTORS.

THE FIFTY COFFINS ABOARD THE DEMETER!

PRECISELY.

BY NOW, DRACULA WILL HAVE HAVE SECURED THEM. I FEAR HIS PLANS ARE LONG LAID.

BUT WE MUST FIND THEM --

BUT DOCTOR VAN HELSING...

?!?

... I KNOW EXACTLY WHERE THEY ARE!

I SHOULD KNOW... I MADE THE ARRANGEMENTS FOR EVERY ESTATE PURCHASE, CUSTOMS FEE, AND SHIPPING RECEIPT THE COUNT REQUIRED! FIFTY COFFINS, BILLED AS PERSONAL ITEMS...

... SHIPPED BY THE SCHOONER DEMETER...

... THEN CRATED TO TWENTY THREE PROPERTIES THROUGHOUT LONDON AND YORKSHIRE. BILLINGTON & PATTERSON CLAIMED THE CARGO THAT WAS RECOVERED FROM THE SHIP, AND ARRANGED FOR CARTERS TO TAKE THE COFFINS TO THEIR FINAL DESTINATIONS.

HERE, GENTLEMEN, ARE COMPLETE RECORDS OF THE VARIOUS TRANSACTIONS, AND ALSO THE ADDRESSES... AS DR. VAN HELSING REQUESTED IN HIS CABLE!

THMP!

IMPRESSIVE, MR. HARKER.

NO DOUBT YOU MAKE A FIRST-RATE ESTATE AGENT...

... BUT DO YOU HAVE THE NERVES TO WORK AGAINST THIS...

... THIS COUNT DRACULA?

I FACED MY FEARS IN TRANSYLVANIA...

KNOWING IT WAS NOT ALL SOME... NIGHTMARE HAS RESTORED ME! AND WHEN THE TIME --

BLAM! BLAM!

AAI!!!

WHAT THE DEVIL?

IT'S MORRIS! QUINCY, WHAT ARE YOU DOING OUT THERE?

WHEW!

I'M FINE!

SORRY FOR THE FUSS, FOLKS...

SAW A BAT FLAPPING AT THE WINDOW, JUST BEFORE THE HARKERS ARRIVED...

... SO I CAME OUT HERE TO TAKE A SHOT AT IT.

LET US HOPE IT IS BUT A COINCIDENCE. STILL, MR. HARKER'S PAPERS PROVE WHAT I HAD SUSPECTED...

A... BAT?

... WHAT THE BAT MAY CONFIRM...

... ONE OF DRACULA'S LAIRS IS NEARBY...

THAT SO?

... AT CAIRFAX ABBEY!

ANOTHER SUSPICION THAT IS PROVED!

WELL, I HAVE MADE THE PREPARATIONS FOR THIS MOMENT...

... I HAVE HERE AGAIN THE NECESSARY INSTRUMENTS, WE HAD BETTER SET OUT TO CARFAX AT ONCE!

I'M GLAD I WORE A SENSIBLE DRESS!

BUT MINA! I COULDN'T POSSIBLY LET YOU COME ON THIS BUSINESS! IT WOULD BE BETTER TO KNOW YOU WERE SAFE IN BED...

WHAT?

MY FRIEND... IT OCCURS TO ME THAT YOUR PATIENT RENFIELD, WITH HIS BLOOD MANIA, IS MIXED INTO THIS AFFAIR...

IT IS POSSIBLE...

I'D BETTER SEE HIM, THEN... AND HOPE THAT HE IS IN A TALKATIVE MOOD!

MADAME MINA... IF YOU WISH TO BE INVOLVED, PERHAPS YOU WOULD LIKE TO GO WITH DR. SEWARD?

CERTAINLY!

I'M AFRAID THERE WAS NO SENSE TO BE HAD FROM RENFIELD....

... ALTHOUGH HIS MANNER GREATLY CONCERNS ME!

HOW FARES OUR ATTEMPT AT HOUSE-BREAKING?

HNPH! BREAKING THIS LOCK IS A TRICKY BUSINESS..!

BUT I'VE BEEN TRYING TO TELL YOU...

... I TOOK THE PRE-CAUTION OF MAKING A DUPLICATE KEY!

!

A FIRST-RATE ESTATE AGENT IS ALWAYS PREPARED.

THE STENCH OF THIS PLACE IS UNBEARABLE! QUICKLY, WE MUST FIND THOSE PARTS OF THE ABBEY GIVEN OVER TO DRACULA'S LAIR!

WELL, THERE IS CERTAINLY NO QUESTION OF THIS BEING THE RIGHT PLACE!

GLK!

THEY HAVE FOUND MY HOME...

WHAT HAVE YOU TOLD THEM, SLAVE?

I HAVE PROMISED YOU MANY SPIDERS... YES, AND OTHER FLESH THAT IS GOOD...

...BUT YOU HAVE EARNED NOTHING!

WE'VE FOUND THEM! BACK HERE!

EXCELLENT!

QUICKLY! WE SHALL MAKE THESE COFFINS UNUSABLE TO THE UN-DEAD.

PIECES OF COMMUNION WAFER, WITH A BLESSING FROM ROME... THESE TURN HIS COFFINS AGAINST HIS UNHOLY ABUSE...

BUT FURTHER, LET US TAKE THE STENCH OF UN-DEAD FROM THESE HALLS FOREVER!

AH!

SO THEY WORK AGAINST ME... THOUGH THEIR STRUGGLING LIVES ARE A HEARTBEAT TO ONE WHO LIVES ON THROUGH THE AGES!

BUT STILL...

... I CANNOT YET RISK OPEN CONFLICT IN THIS STRANGE LAND...

... MY PLANS ARE NOT FULLY RIPE!

BAH! THERE IS TIME TO SEE WHAT SCHEMES THEY WORK AGAINST ME IN THIS HOUSE...

YOU... YOU INVITED ME INTO THIS HOUSE, WHEN IT WOULD HAVE BEEN BARRED AGAINST ME. YOUR GREED HAS SERVED ME WELL...

M-MASTER...

... AND NOW YOU MAY CLAIM YOUR REWARD.

IN TRUTH, WE TOOK UPON OURSELVES A TERRIBLE RISK, TO ENTER THAT DEVIL'S HOUSE AT NIGHT! BUT THE THREAT JUSTIFIED ANY DANGER.

NOW, AS DAWN APPROACHES, WE NEED BUT TAKE A FEW HOURS SAFE REST...

... AND THEN STAMP OUT EVERY NEST OF THIS UN-DEAD BEFORE NIGHT MAKES ITS RETURN!

I MUST SAY, MR. HARKER, WHEN DR. VAN HELSING TOLD US OF YOUR COURAGE, HE UNDERSTATED THE MATTER!

AND LOOK! YOUR WIFE HAS BEEN WAITING FOR US... SHE HAS LEFT HER LAMP BURNING...

!

MINA!

QUICKLY! QUICKLY!!!

THAT IS HIS MARK YOU SEE BURNING!

HE -- HE'S GONE!

YES. THE UN-DEAD,, HIS STRENGTH IS IN SECRECY! HE MUST FLEE, TO MAKE NEW PLANS...

MINA?!?

...

DOCTOR VAN HELSING... WHAT'S WRONG WITH MINA? SHE'S NOT...

NOT...

DARK-NESS...

NO, MY FRIEND...

...NOT YET.

AH!

BUT -- CAN IT BE?

WATER...

THE UN-DEAD, HE SEEKS TO WORK A NEW REVENGE UPON US! DRACULA HAS FED MADAME MINA OF HIS OWN BLOOD, TO BIND HER TO HIM! ALREADY, SHE BEGINS TO SEE WHAT HE SEES, HEAR WHAT HE HEARS.

SHE HAS HIS POISON SO DEEP IN HER VEINS, EVEN A BLOOD TRANSFUSION WOULD BE ONLY TEMPORARY RELIEF! UNLESS DRACULA IS SOON AND UTTERLY DESTROYED, SHE WILL WEAKEN AS LUCY DID, AND BECOME A VAMPIRE!

NO!

BUT WAIT! IN HIS EAGERNESS TO TORMENT US, DRACULA MAKES A GRAVE MISTAKE. THIS UN-HOLY BOND, IT DRAWS HER SOUL TO HIM, BUT WITH THE HYPNOTISM OF MESMER, WE CAN FOLLOW THEIR LINK ...

... BACK TO HIM!

WHAT...

WHAT HAPPENED?

3 OCTOBER -- I HAD NEVER THOUGHT TO WRITE IN THIS JOURNAL AGAIN...

... BUT STRANGE EVENTS HAVE OVERTAKEN US ALL, AND I STRUGGLE TO KEEP THEM CLEAR.

WHAT DO YOU SEE, MY CHILD?

NOTHING...

... BUT I HEAR WATER... WAVES...

... AND SEAGULLS...

THE DOCKS?

OF COURSE! HIS PLANS ARE NOT RIPE...

12 OCTOBER, PARIS -- DR. VAN HELSING HAS INDEED BEEN ABLE TO HYPNOTIZE MINA, AND MOST EASILY AT THE DAWN AND TWILIGHT HOURS WHEN NATURE IS AT ITS MOST UNCERTAIN.

... AND SO HE FLEES TO TRANSYLVANIA, TO PREPARE ANEW!

... AGAIN, WATER... THE CREAKING OF SAILS...

14 OCTOBER, BUDA-PEST -- IT IS FORTUNATE THAT DRACULA HAS TAKEN THE SEA-ROUTE TO ROMANIA. IT IS SAFER FOR HIS PURPOSES...

... BUT THE ORIENT EXPRESS SHALL TAKE US THERE FIRST!

WAVES AGAIN... SALTY AIR...

DIFFERENT... SMELL... SOIL... WOOD...

... CREAKING BOARDS OF... A CART?

MINA?

30 OCTOBER, BORGO PASS -- WE ARE CLOSE...

SO! DRACULA HAS COME AGAIN INTO THIS COUNTRY, HE IS BEING CARRIED THROUGH THE MOUNTAINS BY SLEIGH OR HORSE-CART...
... ANOTHER DAY, AT MOST, AND HE WILL BE HERE!
MR. MORRIS HAS MADE OUR PLANS.
EXCELLENT! IT WILL BE YOUR WORK TO STOP THE COUNT ON THE HIGH ROAD. MADAME MINA AND I SHALL STAY BEHIND, TO TAKE OTHER PRECAUTIONS...
BUT MINA --
DO NOT FEAR, FRIEND JONATHAN! I PLACE THIS WAFER OF THE SACRED HOST AGAINST HER FOREHEAD...
TO PROTECT HER FROM THE DAR --
PWF!
AH!
GASP!
QUICKLY! THE POWER OF DRAC-ULA GROWS OVER MISS MINA! BY TOMORROW'S SUNSET, IT WILL BE TOO LATE! YOU MUST GO NOW!
NO!
STAY WITH VAN HELSING, DARLING! AND STAY STRONG...
JACK! MR. HOLMWOOD! MR. MORRIS!
WE WILL DESTROY THE MONSTER BEFORE ANOTHER DAY IS OUT!

ALMOST *HUFF!* THERE!

WHEN JONATHAN TOLD ME TO STAY SAFE...

... WITH YOU...

... I DON'T THINK THIS IS WHAT HE HAD IN MIND!

AH WELL!

KEEP A WATCH OUT HERE, THAT IS AS SAFE AS ANYWHERE IN THIS LAND...

... AND USE THE ELEPHANT-GUN IN NEED!

AH... THIS JOURNAL OF HARKER'S, IT IS TRULY A MARVEL!

EVERY DETAIL IS PRECISE...

... PRECISE, AND CORRECT! THIS MUST BE THE PLACE.

IT DOES LITTLE GOOD TO KILL THE SERPENT...

HRNG!

... IF THE BROOD REMAIN!

FAUGH! SUCH A FOUL REMNANT OF WHAT WAS ONCE FAIR!

SIGH!

!

THNNNK!

IT IS DONE. A DAY SPENT IN FILTHY WORK, BUT NOW GARLIC AND SUNLIGHT MUST MAKE PURE THIS BLOODIED PLACE... AND AS FOR THE CRYPT OF DRACU--

BLAM!

MINA!

IS IT TOO LATE, THEN?

BLAM!

AAIYEE!

MISSED!

EH?

AROOOo!

AROOOO!

QUICKLY! THEY ARE GOING TO THE COUNT!

THERE ARE HUNDREDS OF THEM!

THEY ARE HEADING DOWN INTO A SORT OF VALLEY... THE BORGO PASS, I THINK.

THERE ARE PEOPLE...

AND ALSO HORSES... AND --

DRACULA!

TOO LATE...

GLK!

!

KOF! KOF!

ENOUGH!

EVEN THIS FIEND CAN BLEED IN THE SUN- LIGHT...

HARKER! GET OUT OF THE WAY, MAN!

HUFF! HUFF!

EXCELLENT SHOOTING, MRS. HARKER!

PERHAPS...

... BUT I HAD BEEN AIMING FOR THE COFFIN!

?

FAREWELL, MR. MORRIS ...

6 NOVEMBER, BORGO PASS -- WE WANT NO PROOFS, WE ASK NO ONE TO BELIEVE US...

... IT IS ENOUGH THAT THE NIGHT-MARE IS ENDED...

... AND A NEW DAY BEGINS!

VLAD DRACULA TEPES (1431-1476) WAS A REAL PERSON. HE WAS NOT A COUNT -- IN FACT, HE WAS PRINCE OF WALLACHIA (A SMALL PRINCIPALITY IN MODERN ROMANIA), WHO OWED HIS CROWN TO THE KING OF HUNGARY.

IN THE FIFTEENTH CENTURY, THE TURKISH EMPIRE SWEPT THROUGH EASTERN EUROPE AND THREATENED MANY SMALL STATES LIKE WALLACHIA. AT THE SAME TIME, WALLACHIA ITSELF WAS TORN APART BY CIVIL WARS BETWEEN RIVALS IN THE ROYAL FAMILY. VLAD DRACUL WAS DRIVEN OUT OF THE COUNTRY, AND HIS SON DRACULA WAS BORN IN EXILE IN NEARBY TRANSYLVANIA.

IN THOSE TREACHEROUS TIMES, DRACULA BEGAN TO LEARN THE KNIGHTLY PROFESSION FROM WALLACHIAN BOYARS (ARISTOCRATS) AT THE AGE OF FIVE. HE WAS LATER SENT TO LIVE IN THE TURKISH SULTAN'S COURT AS A TEEN.

DRACULA FOUGHT MANY BLOODY WARS TO RECLAIM HIS FATHER'S THRONE. SOMETIMES HE WAS ALLIED WITH THE TURKS, SOMETIMES THE HUNGARIANS, BUT HIS ENEMIES WERE ALWAYS HIS ROYAL RELATIVES, AND THE BOYARS AND MERCHANTS WHO SUPPORTED THEM.

DRACULA WAS ONE OF THE CRUELEST MEN IN A CRUEL AGE. HE EARNED THE NICKNAME TEPES ("THE IMPALER") FROM HIS FAVORITE METHOD OF EXECUTION. IN THE 1450'S, HE WAS POWERFUL ENOUGH TO FIGHT FOR INDEPENDENCE AGAINST HIS TURKISH ALLIES.

BUT DRACULA'S EXTREME METHODS COULD NEVER COMPLETELY SECURE HIS RULE. HE WAS DRIVEN OUT OF WALLACHIA SEVERAL TIMES BY RIVALS AND REBELLIOUS BOYARS, FIGHTING HIS WAY BACK EVERY TIME. FINALLY, THE TURKS INVADED IN 1476, AND DRACULA WAS KILLED AT BUCHAREST.

VLAD DRACULA WAS NOTORIOUS THROUGHOUT EUROPE FOR HIS STRENGTH AND CRUELTY. BUT MODERN-DAY ROMANIANS REMEMBER HIM AS A NATIONAL HERO WHO FREED THEM FROM FOREIGN RULE.

ABRAHAM "BRAM" STOKER (1847-1912) WAS BORN IN DUBLIN, IRELAND. AFTER A SICKLY CHILDHOOD, STOKER ATTENDED TRINITY COLLEGE, THEN TOOK A JOB AS A CIVIL SERVANT.

BRAM STOKER WROTE NEWS ARTICLES AND SHORT STORIES IN HIS SPARE TIME, AND IN 1878 BECAME THE MANAGER OF THE LYCEUM THEATRE IN LONDON.

BUT WHILE STOKER WROTE MANY NOVELS AND PRODUCED MANY PLAYS, HIS MOST FAMOUS WORK WAS "DRACULA." BEGUN UNDER THE TITLE "THE UN-DEAD" IN 1894, IT WAS PUBLISHED IN 1897 AND BECAME AN INSTANT HIT. STOKER WENT ON TO WRITE AND PRODUCE A DRACULA PLAY, AND CONTINUED WITH OTHER HORROR AND ADVENTURE NOVELS INCLUDING "THE JEWEL OF THE SEVEN STARS," "LAIR OF THE WHITE WORM," AND SEVERAL SHORT DRACULA STORIES.

BRAM STOKER'S DRACULA IS THE MOST IMITATED MODERN HORROR STORY; IT HAS SPAWNED HUNDREDS OF FILM, BOOK, GAME, AND COMIC BOOK ADAPTATIONS, AND WAS THE INSPIRATION FOR OTHER HORROR CLASSICS LIKE THE GERMAN SILENT FILM "NOSFERATU."

VAMPIRE STORIES WERE POPULAR IN VICTORIAN ENGLAND (1837-1901). ORIGINALLY IMPORTED FROM EASTERN EUROPE, THESE GHOSTLY CHARACTERS BECAME THE STAPLE OF CHEAP "PENNY DREADFUL" MAGAZINES, WITH "VARNEY THE VAMPIRE" TERRORIZING ENGLISH READERS IN THE 1840S.

BUT WHILE "DRACULA" IS A VICTORIAN NOVEL, IT IS SET AT THE DAWN OF A NEW AGE. THE HEROES USE TELEGRAMS, ELECTRIC LANTERNS, TYPEWRITERS, AND DICTAPHONES. THERE WERE ALREADY THOUSANDS OF AUTOMOBILES IN EUROPE AND AMERICA IN 1897, AND ELECTRIC LIGHTS WERE STARTING TO BRIGHTEN THE CITIES. MODERN MEDICINE, IN THE FORM OF HYPNOTISM (OR "MESMERISM") AND BLOOD TRANSFUSIONS, IS JUST ONE OF MANY MODERN TOOLS STOKER'S HEROES USE AGAINST THE ANCIENT SORCERY OF THE VAMPIRE KING.